Contents

Day and night

It is **day** when the sky is light and the sun is out. During the day, most grown-ups get out of bed and go to work. Children go to school.

It is **night** when the sky is dark and the moon is out. Most people go to bed at night.

(1) Sophie is getting ready for school. What should she do?
Tick the correct pictures.

Get dressed

Have breakfast

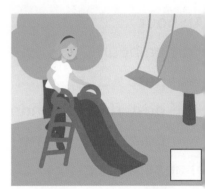
Play on the slide

(2) Amir is getting ready for bed. What should he do?
Tick the correct pictures.

Paint a picture

Put on pyjamas

Listen to a story

Did you know?

Day and night happen because the earth spins. When the part of the world you are in faces the sun, it is daytime.

Schofield&Sims

Telling the Time 1

Name

Note for teachers and parents

Learning to tell the time is a complex process that many children need help to grasp. This series breaks down telling the time into very small steps that every child can understand. Featuring clear step-by-step learning, varied practice activities and fun time facts, these workbooks provide everything children need to master this essential life skill.

Telling the Time 1 introduces children to 'o'clock', 'half past', 'quarter past' and 'quarter to' and how these times relate to simple fractions. It also teaches about time in a broader sense, including units of time, times of the day, days of the week, months of the year and the seasons. This book supports the National Curriculum for Mathematics at Key Stage 1, but it can also be used with older children who require additional support.

Try to discuss time as often as you can with the child and draw attention to different means of time-telling such as a clock on the wall, a wristwatch or time displays on phones and computers. Questions such as "What time is bedtime?" and "How long does it take to get to school?" will help the child to think about the importance of time measurement and to become familiar with vocabulary that relates to time.

Each book features large clock faces that little fingers can easily count on. When introducing each new time, encourage the child to count aloud and point to the numbers around the edge of the clock. This will help to secure the idea that the hands of the clock are constantly moving around the circle of the clock face. The hands of the clock are colour-coded throughout the series – blue for the minute hand and red for the hour hand – to help the child to identify them quickly.

Children are given frequent opportunities to practise their learning through a variety of activities, such as drawing the hands on the clock, matching activities, and word and number problems. You will find answers to all the activities at the back of the book.

Published by **Schofield & Sims Ltd**, 7 Mariner Court, Wakefield, West Yorkshire WF4 3FL, UK
Telephone 01484 607080
www.schofieldandsims.co.uk

This edition copyright © Schofield & Sims Ltd, 2017
First published in 2017
Third impression 2020

Author: **Christine Shaw**
Christine Shaw has asserted her moral rights under the Copyright, Designs and Patents Act, 1988, to be identified as the author of this work.

British Library Cataloguing in Publication Data
A catalogue record for this book is available from the British Library.

Design by **Oxford Designers & Illustrators Ltd**
Illustration by **Maria Chiara Banchini** at **Lemonade Illustration Agency**

Printed in the UK by **Page Bros (Norwich) Ltd**

ISBN 978 07217 1418 9

Times of the day

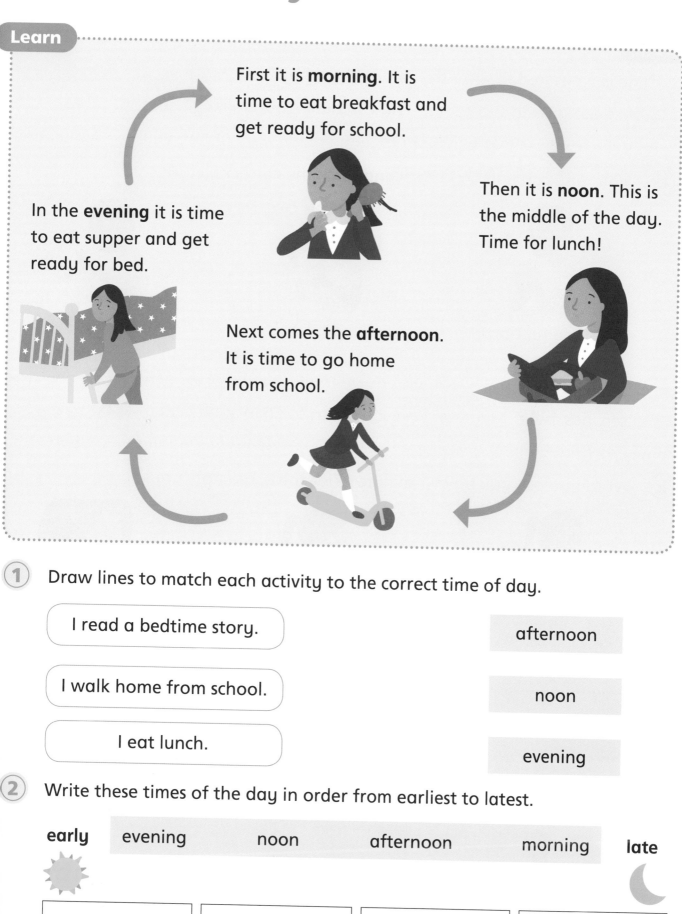

First it is **morning**. It is time to eat breakfast and get ready for school.

Then it is **noon**. This is the middle of the day. Time for lunch!

In the **evening** it is time to eat supper and get ready for bed.

Next comes the **afternoon**. It is time to go home from school.

1 Draw lines to match each activity to the correct time of day.

I read a bedtime story.   afternoon

I walk home from school.   noon

I eat lunch.   evening

2 Write these times of the day in order from earliest to latest.

early   evening   noon   afternoon   morning   late

Units of time

Time is measured in **seconds, minutes** and **hours**.

A **second** is a very short time. You can blink your eyes in 1 second.

(1) What else can you do in 1 second? Tick the correct picture.

Clap your hands   Read a book   Bake a cake

60 seconds make 1 **minute**. You can count to 60 in 1 minute.

(2) What else can you do in 1 minute? Tick the correct picture.

Sneeze   Eat an apple   Watch a film

60 minutes make 1 **hour**. You can have your lunch break in 1 hour.

(3) What else can you do in 1 hour? Tick the correct picture.

Jump in the air   Get a bus to town   Sing a song

Quick and slow

Time can be **quick** or **slow**.

A **second** is very quick.

A **minute** is slower than a second but quicker than an **hour**.

An **hour** is slower than a minute but quicker than a **day**.

1 Write the units of time in order from quickest to slowest.

quick

minute	day	hour	second

slow

2 Who was quicker? Tick the winner of the race.

30 seconds

2 hours

3 **Quicker** or **slower**? Write the correct word in each sentence.

A day is _____ than an hour.

Running is _____ than walking.

A second is _____ than an hour.

A millisecond is even quicker than a second. There are 1000 milliseconds in a second. Milliseconds can be used to find the winner in a very close race.

Clocks

You can use a **clock** to tell the time. There are many different types of clocks.

wristwatch   alarm clock   grandfather clock   stopwatch

sundial   pocket watch   cuckoo clock   egg timer

Most phones, computers and ovens also have clocks.

(1) How many clocks can you see in this picture? _____

The sun was the first clock. When it rose in the sky in the morning, people woke up. When it went down in the evening, people went to bed.

Numbers and hands

A traditional clock has a **face** and **hands**. The clock face has numbers from **1** to **12**.

1 Count aloud the numbers around the clock face.

Write the missing numbers.

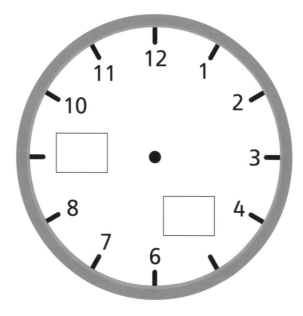

A clock has a big hand and a small hand.

The small hand points to the hours and the big hand points to the minutes.

O'clock

On this clock the small hand points to 5.
When the big hand points straight up to 12, it shows o'clock.
This clock shows 5 o'clock.

This clock shows 12 o'clock.
The small hand and the big hand both point to 12.

Did you know?

In the olden days, people used to say, "It is 6 of the clock." These days people just say, "It is 6 o'clock."

O'clock: draw the hands

(1) Draw the small hand on the clock to show 3 o'clock.
Make sure the small hand is shorter than the big hand.

(2) Draw the big hand and the small hand on the clock to show 10 o'clock.

O'clock: tell the time

① What time is it?

It is _____ o'clock.

It is _____ o'clock.

It is _____ o'clock.

It is _____ o'clock.

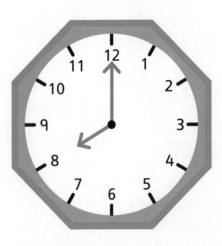

It is _____ o'clock.

It is _____ o'clock.

O'clock: tell the time

(2) Draw lines to match each clock to the correct time.

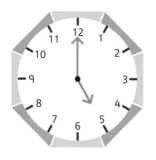

It is 11 o'clock.

It is 3 o'clock.

It is 5 o'clock.

(3) Read each clock and write the time below the picture.

It is _____.   It is _____.

An hour

The big hand and the small hand always go clockwise around the clock face.

Count aloud the numbers on the clock face. Start at 12 and go all the way around to 12 again.

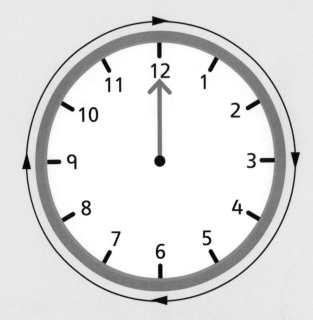

The big hand takes an hour to go all the way around the clock from 12 and back to 12 again.

1 Colour in the whole clock face to show an hour.

Half an hour

A clock face can be split into 2 halves. Each half shows **half an hour**.

It takes half an hour for the **big hand** to go halfway around the clock from **12** to **6**.

When the **big hand** points to **6**, it shows **half past**.

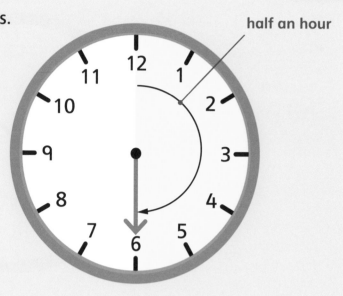

half an hour

① Tick the shapes that show a half shaded.

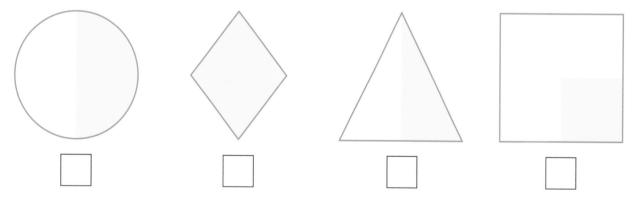

② Colour in half of the clock face to show half an hour.

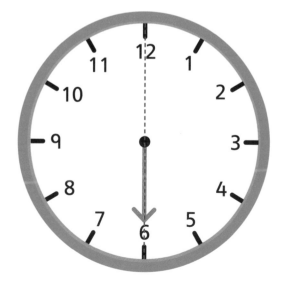

Half past

This clock shows **half past 1**.

The **big hand** is halfway around the clock and it points straight down to **6**. Can you see what has happened to the **small hand**? It is halfway between **1** and **2**.

This clock shows **half past 4**.

The **big hand** points to **6**.
The **small hand** is halfway between **4** and **5**.

Did you know?

There are 30 minutes in half an hour.

Half past: draw the hands

1 Draw the hands on the clock to show half past 7.
Can you see where to put the small hand?

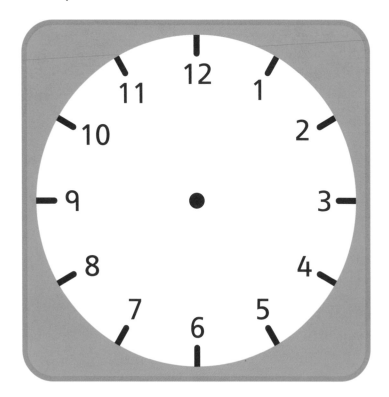

2 Draw the hands on the clock to show half past 9.

Half past: tell the time

1 What time is it?

It is half past _____.

It is half past _____.

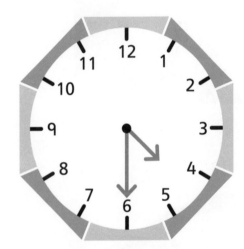

It is half past _____.

It is half past _____.

It is half past _____.

It is half past _____.

Half past: tell the time

(2) Draw lines to match each clock to the correct time.

It is half past 10.

It is half past 5.

It is half past 1.

(3) Read each clock and write the time below the picture.

It is _____.   It is _____.

Time sequences 1

(1) Add the missing times to each sequence.

8 o'clock, 9 o'clock, 10 o'clock, _____, _____

2 o'clock, 3 o'clock, 4 o'clock, _____, _____

(2) Draw the hands on the clock to show the missing time in this sequence.

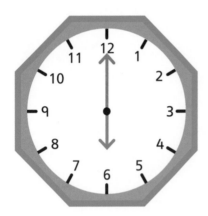  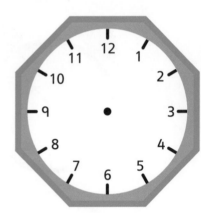

(3) Add the missing times to each sequence.

1 o'clock, half past 1, 2 o'clock, _____, _____

4 o'clock, half past 4, 5 o'clock, _____, _____

12 o'clock, half past 12, _____, _____

(4) **Earlier** or **later**? Write the correct word in each sentence. All these times are in the morning.

4 o'clock is _____ than 5 o'clock.

8 o'clock is _____ than 6 o'clock.

Half past 10 is _____ than 10 o'clock.

Half past 2 is _____ than half past 3.

Quarter of an hour

A clock face can be split into 4 quarters. Each quarter shows a **quarter of an hour**.

It takes a quarter of an hour for the big hand to go a quarter of the way around the clock from 12 to 3.

When the big hand points to 3, it shows quarter past.

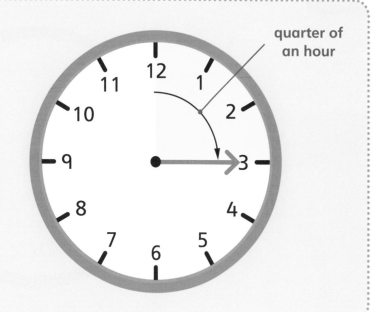

quarter of an hour

1 Tick the shapes that show a quarter shaded.

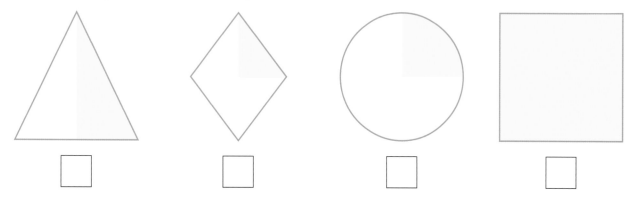

2 Colour in a quarter of the clock face to show a quarter of an hour.

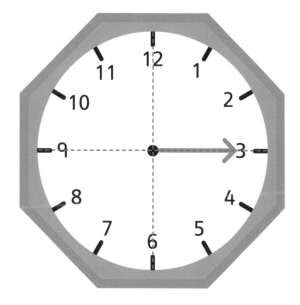

Quarter past

This clock shows quarter past 7.

The big hand is a quarter of the way around the clock and it points to 3.
Can you see what has happened to the small hand? It is a quarter of
the way between 7 and 8.

This clock shows quarter past 10.

The big hand points to 3.
The small hand is a quarter of the way between 10 and 11.

Did you know?

There are 15 minutes in a quarter of an hour.

Quarter past: draw the hands

1 Draw the hands on the clock to show quarter past 6.
Can you see where to put the small hand?

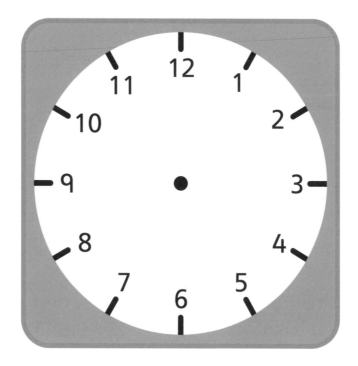

2 Draw the hands on the clock to show quarter past 11.

Quarter past: tell the time

1 What time is it?

It is quarter past _____ .

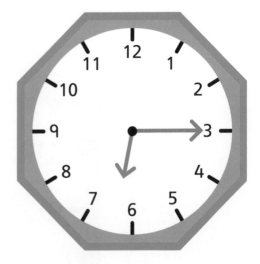

It is quarter past _____ .

It is quarter past _____ .

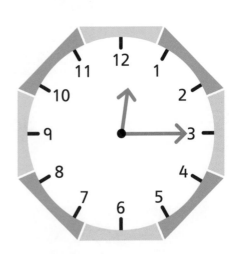

It is quarter past _____ .

It is quarter past _____ .

It is quarter past _____ .

More quarters

Remember, when the big hand is halfway around the clock, it shows half past.

When the big hand is a quarter of the way around the clock, it shows quarter past.

When the big hand points to 9, it has a quarter of the way to go until the next o'clock. This shows quarter to.

quarter of an hour

(1) Tick the circles that show a quarter shaded.

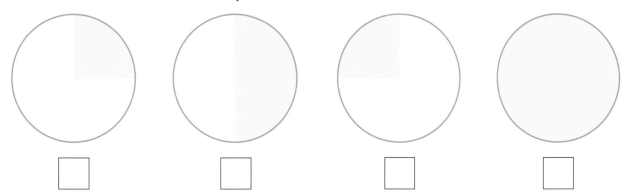

Quarter to

This clock shows quarter to 5.

The big hand is nearly all the way around the clock and it points to 9.
It has a quarter of the way to go until the next o'clock.
Can you see what has happened to the small hand? It is nearly at 5.

This clock shows quarter to 11.

The big hand points to 9. The small hand is nearly at 11.

Did you know?

In many countries around the world, people eat a snack at about 11 o'clock to keep them going until lunch. In English, this is called 'elevenses'.

Quarter to: draw the hands

1 Draw the hands on the clock to show quarter to 7.
Can you see where to put the small hand?

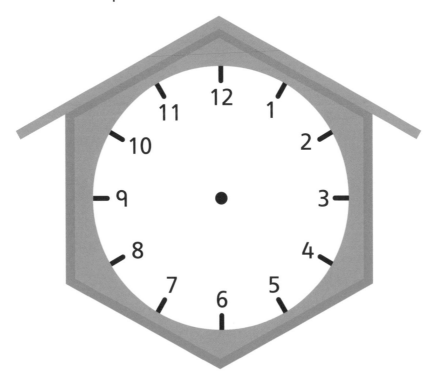

2 Draw the hands on the clock to show quarter to 4.

Quarter to: tell the time

1 What time is it?

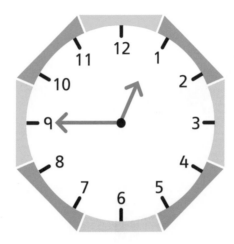

It is quarter to _____.

It is quarter to _____.

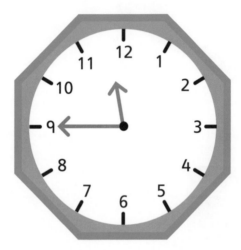

It is quarter to _____.

It is quarter to _____.

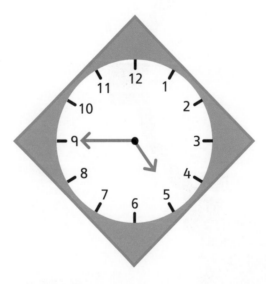

It is quarter to _____.

It is quarter to _____.

Time sequences 2

1 Add the missing times to each sequence.

2 o'clock, quarter past 2, _____ , _____

quarter to 8, 8 o'clock, _____ , _____

half past 11, quarter to 12, _____ , _____

quarter past 5, half past 5, _____ , _____

2 Draw the hands on the clock to show the missing time in this sequence.

3 **Earlier** or **later**? Write the correct word in each sentence. All these times are at night.

9 o'clock is _____ than 7 o'clock.

12 o'clock is _____ than half past 12.

Quarter past 10 is _____ than 10 o'clock.

8 o'clock is _____ than quarter to 8.

Mixed practice: draw the hands

1 Draw the hands on each clock to show the correct time.

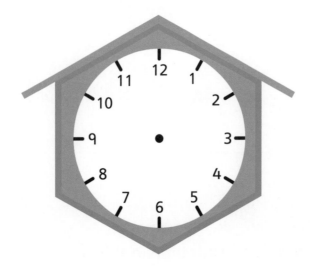

It is 9 o'clock.

It is half past 2.

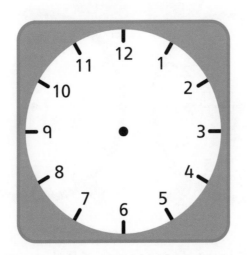

It is quarter past 4.

It is quarter past 10.

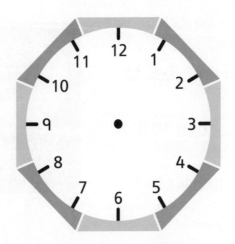

It is quarter to 3.

It is quarter to 6.

Mixed practice: tell the time

1 What time is it?

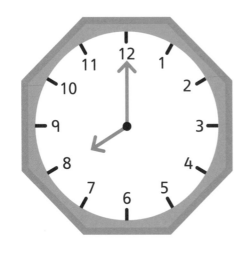

It is _____.

It is _____.

It is _____.

It is _____.

It is _____.

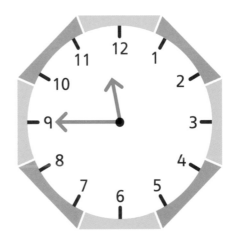

It is _____.

Days of the week

Time is also measured in **days** and **weeks**.

There are **7** days in a week:

Monday   **Tuesday**   **Wednesday**   **Thursday**   **Friday**
Saturday   **Sunday**

The days from Monday to Friday are called **weekdays**.
Saturday and Sunday are **weekend** days.

1   Look at the diary.
Draw lines to match the day of the week to the correct picture.

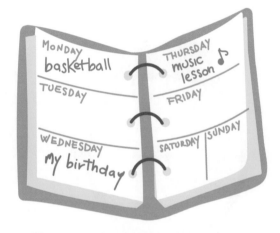

Wednesday

Thursday

Monday

2   Write the correct day of the week to complete each sentence.

_____ comes after Monday.

_____ comes after Thursday.

_____ and _____ are

weekend days.

_____ comes before Thursday.

Did you know?

Sunday is named after the sun and Monday is named after the moon.

Yesterday, today and tomorrow

Today is the day it is <u>now</u>.

Yesterday is the day before today.

Tomorrow is the day after today.

← Yesterday

Today

Tomorrow →

1 What day is it today?

Today it is _____ .

2 Write a few words to complete each sentence.

Yesterday I ate _____ .

Today I am wearing _____ .

Tomorrow I will go _____ .

3 Write the correct day of the week to answer the questions.

Today is Saturday. What day was it yesterday?

_____

Today is Wednesday. What day will it be tomorrow?

_____

Yesterday was Sunday. What day is it today?

_____

Tomorrow is Thursday. What day is it today?

_____

Months of the year

Time is also measured in **months** and **years**.

There are **12** months in a year:

January	**February**	**March**	**April**
May	**June**	**July**	**August**
September	**October**	**November**	**December**

1 Look at this word jumble. Some months are missing.

Write the missing months on the lines.

January April
August February
December
November June
May September

_____

_____

_____

2 Write the correct month to complete each sentence.

_____ comes after March.

_____ comes before July.

_____ is the fifth month of the year.

My birthday is in _____ .

Did you know?

Many of the months are named after Roman gods. March is named after Mars, the god of war. June is named after Juno, the goddess of marriage.

Calendars

Calendars show the days, weeks and months of the year.

This page of the calendar shows January.

1 Look at the calendar. Answer these questions.

On what day of the week does January start? _____

On what day of the week does January end? _____

How many Fridays are there in this month? _____

On what day of the week is Finn's birthday? _____

On what day of the week is swimming? _____

On what day of the week is football? _____

Seasons

Each year has **4 seasons**: winter   spring   summer   autumn

December, January and February are **winter** months. The weather is often cold and sometimes it snows in winter.

(1) Tick the activities that people often do in winter.

Keep warm   Drink hot drinks   Go camping

March, April and May are **spring** months. The weather is warmer but there is often rain. Flowers grow in spring.

(2) Tick the activities that people often do in spring.

Play outside   Build a snowman   See baby animals

Did you know?

When it is summer in the northern part of the earth, it is winter in the southern part. In Australia they celebrate Christmas on the beach!

Seasons

June, July and August are **summer** months. The weather is often hot and sunny in summer.

③ Help Safa pack a bag for the beach on a summer day.

Tick the things she needs.

September, October and November are **autumn** months. The weather is colder and there is often rain. The trees begin to lose their leaves.

④ Help Josh get ready to go out on a rainy day in autumn.

Tick the things he needs.

⑤ **Summer** or **winter**? Write the correct word in each sentence.

_____ is the coldest season.

_____ is the hottest season.

Answers

Page 4
1 Get dressed, Have breakfast
2 Put on pyjamas, Listen to a story

Page 5
1 I read a   afternoon
   bedtime story.
   I walk home   noon
   from school.
   I eat lunch.   evening

2 morning noon afternoon evening

Page 6
1 Clap your hands
2 Eat an apple
3 Get a bus to town

Page 7
1 second minute hour day
2 hare
3 slower, quicker, quicker

Page 8
1 5

Page 9
1 The child counts the numbers around the clock in a clockwise direction.
   5, 9

Page 11
1

2

Pages 12–13
1 7 o'clock, 9 o'clock, 2 o'clock, 6 o'clock, 8 o'clock, 12 o'clock

2
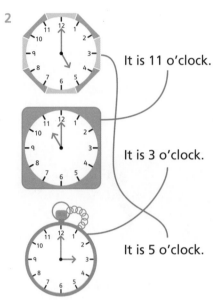
It is 11 o'clock.

It is 3 o'clock.

It is 5 o'clock.

3 4 o'clock, 6 o'clock

Page 14
1 whole clock face coloured in

Page 15
1
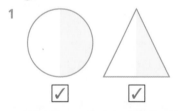
✓   ✓

2 half of clock face coloured in

Page 17
1

2

Pages 18–19
1 half past 2, half past 9, half past 4, half past 11, half past 12, half past 6

2
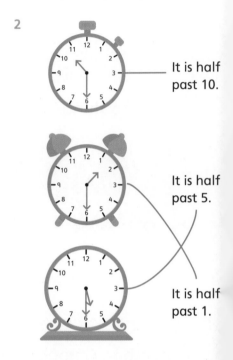
It is half past 10.

It is half past 5.

It is half past 1.

3 half past 2, half past 8

Page 20
1 11 o'clock, 12 o'clock 5 o'clock, 6 o'clock

2

3 half past 2, 3 o'clock half past 5, 6 o'clock 1 o'clock, half past 1
4 earlier, later, later, earlier

Page 21
1
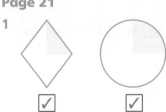
✓   ✓

2 any quarter of clock face coloured in

Answers

ge 23

ge 24

quarter past 8, quarter past 6,
quarter past 5, quarter past 12,
quarter past 1, quarter past 4

ge 25

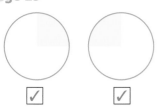

ge 27

ge 28

quarter to 1, quarter to 6,
quarter to 12, quarter to 2,
quarter to 5, quarter to 9

ge 29

half past 2, quarter to 3
quarter past 8, half past 8
12 o'clock, quarter past 12
quarter to 6, 6 o'clock

2

3 later, earlier, later, later

Page 30

1

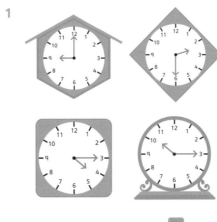

Page 31

1 8 o'clock, half past 7,
quarter past 1, quarter past 6,
quarter to 2, quarter to 12

Page 32

1

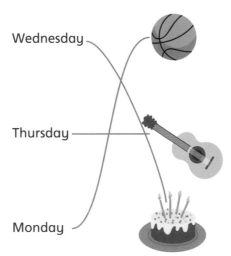

2 Tuesday, Friday, Saturday,
Sunday, Wednesday

Page 33

1 Answers will vary – the day it
is today.

2 Answers will vary.

3 Friday, Thursday, Monday,
Wednesday

Page 34

1 March, July, October

2 April, June, May, answers will
vary

Page 35

1 Monday, Wednesday, 4,
Friday, Saturday, Thursday

Pages 36–37

1 Keep warm, Drink hot drinks

2 Play outside, See baby animals

3

4

5 winter, summer

Schofield&Sims

the long-established educational publisher specialising in maths, English and science

Telling the time is a vital life skill. **Schofield & Sims Telling the Time** breaks this difficult topic down into a sequence of manageable ideas that young learners can approach at their own pace. Beginning with child-friendly explanations of times of day and units of time, the series moves on to introduce telling the time on an analogue clock, before progressing to cover a wide range of related concepts, including different ways of measuring and representing time, time expressions and everyday time problems.

Each activity book provides:

- large, clear clock faces for easy counting
- colour-coded hands to aid recognition of hours and minutes
- 'Learn' panels that explain time-telling in simple steps
- fun general-knowledge facts to enrich learning
- targeted practice, including counting activities, matching exercises, and drawing the hands on the clock
- answers to all the practice questions in the book.

Telling the Time 1 meets all the National Curriculum time requirements for Year 1. It covers times of day (morning, noon, afternoon, evening); basic units of time; comparing and sequencing events in chronological order (earlier/later, first/next, yesterday/tomorrow); telling the time to the hour, half hour and quarter hour; the days of the week and months of the year; calendars; and seasons.

Telling the Time 1   ISBN 978 07217 1418 9
Telling the Time 2   ISBN 978 07217 1419 6
Telling the Time 3   ISBN 978 07217 1420 2

Have you tried **Times Tables Practice** by Schofield & Sims?

This series of books gives children extensive practice in all the times tables relevant to their age group, providing enjoyable activities with attractive illustrations that will hold their attention throughout.

MIX
Paper from responsible sources
FSC® C023114

ISBN 978-07217-1418-9

9 780721 714189 >

ISBN 978 07217 1418 9
Key Stage 1
Age range 5–6 years
£3.95 (Retail price)

For further information and to place your order visit
www.schofieldandsims.co.uk or telephone 01484 607080